LOOK AND FIND

Walt Disney's

MICKEY

AND FRIENDS

TIME TWISTERS

Illustrated by Jaime Diaz Studios

Illustration script development by Angelo DeCesare
Lettering by Kelly Hume

Published by
Louis Weber, C.E.O.
Publications International, Ltd.
7373 North Cicero Avenue
Lincolnwood, Illinois 60646

Manufactured in the U.S.A.

8 7 6 5 4 3 2 1

ISBN 0-7853-0104-6

Look & Find is a trademark of
Publications International, Ltd.

PUBLICATIONS INTERNATIONAL, LTD.

Mickey and his pals are spending a rainy afternoon exploring Ye Olde Curiosity Shoppe. Mickey is peering into a strange mirror when he is bumped into it—*really* into it! Mickey's friends can't let him have all the fun and adventure, so they jump in after him!

Before you jump into the mirror, too, try to find these curious old things.

A record player

A stove

An air conditioner

A popcorn popper

An inkpen

A reading lamp

That rotten Hole-in-the-Hat Gang needs a lesson in good manners. And there's a new sheriff in town who's just the one to teach 'em! Mickey and his pals have time-traveled to Dry Gulch just in time to save the day.

Can you find Sheriff Mickey? Can you find these other folks from Dry Gulch?

Sheriff Mickey

Doc Sawbones

Polly Pureheart

Hank Hammersmith

Andrew MacMoneybaggs III

Miss Pell

It is the year 2999, and Robo-Pete is cloning hundreds of naughty Mickeys, Minnies, Goofys, Donalds, and Plutos!

First, find the switch to turn off the Robo-Clone Machine. Then help the gang look for these Robo-Clones.

The switch

Sprocket Mickey

Gyro Goofy

Submarine Donald

Rocket Minnie

Spring-Action Pluto

Next stop, Main Street, USA! It seems to be 1952 and the Saturday matinee has just ended. The kids are all talking about the new movie, *Aliens from the Pistachio Planet*. Or *was* it a movie? Good thing Mickey and his pals are on the scene to send these *real* space aliens home!

Can you find aliens in these flavors?

Orange creme French vanilla

Neapolitan Mint chip

Chocolate

Strawberry

Peppermint swirl

Avast and ahoy! Mickey is about to take a saltwater bath. Can Minnie and the rest of the time travelers rescue him from his perilous perch? Or will Patch-Eye Pete and his scurvy seadogs make him walk the plank?

It is easy to spot Mickey, but can you find these particular pirates?

Slippery Sam

Bilge-Water Betsy

Hard-Headed Harry

Jolly Roger

Pretty-Boy Lloyd

Peg-Leg Peg

Cue-Ball Bob

Come one, come all to see noble Sir Mickey match jousting skills with Sir Foulplay, the dreaded Knight of Cheatham!

Can you find these silly knights in Merrie Olde England?

The Knight of the Kitchen Table

The Knight of the Pool Table

The Knight of the Round Table

The Knight of the Tea Party Table

The Knight of the Changing Table

The Knight of the Multiplication Table

Spells Broken by Merlin

Ye Ox of Oxford vs. Goofy the Unfortunate

Draw Bridge

Rockin' Robin

Rockin' Robin AND HIS Merrie Five

I Love Little John

TAXES

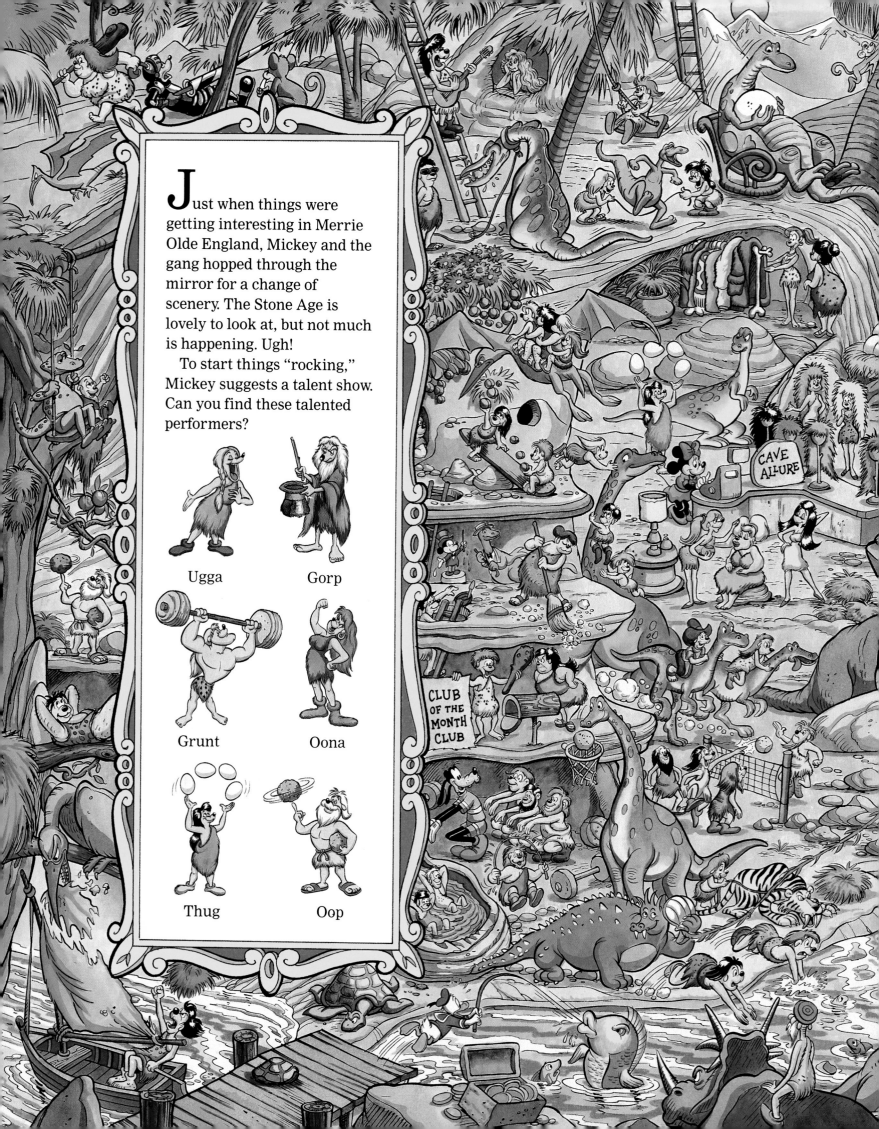

Just when things were getting interesting in Merrie Olde England, Mickey and the gang hopped through the mirror for a change of scenery. The Stone Age is lovely to look at, but not much is happening. Ugh!

To start things "rocking," Mickey suggests a talent show. Can you find these talented performers?

Ugga

Gorp

Grunt

Oona

Thug

Oop

When in Rome, do as the Romans do! That's Mickey's advice to his pals when they find themselves at Caesar's place. The gang is trying to blend in and make small talk, but it's all Greek to them!

Look around Caesar's court. Can you find these Roman things?

XV
This Roman numeral

This Roman goddess

This Roman soldier

A Roman key

This Roman toga

A Roman candle

A Roman bath

MARCH
XV

PORTRAITS
WHILE·U·WAIT

Three cheers for Mickey, Minnie, Donald, Goofy, and Pluto! Their travels through time have made them heroes. Professor Historia has even organized a parade in their honor!

It is easy to spot the five grand marshals, but can you also find these time travelers who slipped through the mirror and followed Mickey home?

An alien

A cowboy

A robot

A pirate

A caveman

A Roman

A knight

DINOSAUR EXHIBIT

Ye Olde CURIOSITY SHOPPE
PROFESSOR HISTORIA, PROP.
BUY   SELL   TRADE
Antiquities
Oddities

GRANDFATHER CLOCK

INAMINUTE

WELCOME HOME TIME TWISTERS

HI MOM!

Go back to Ye Olde Curiosity Shoppe to find curious cats doing these things.

- ☐ Wearing a hat
- ☐ Fishing in a fishbowl
- ☐ Painting a picture
- ☐ Catching a mouse
- ☐ Playing a piano
- ☐ Cracking a safe
- ☐ Reading a book
- ☐ Unknitting a sweater

Pardner, git on back to Dry Gulch to find these things from the wild West.

- ☐ A horse thief
- ☐ A ten-gallon hat
- ☐ A rattlesnake
- ☐ A cow "puncher"
- ☐ Chief Standing Cow
- ☐ A mail-order bride

Go back to the future. Can you find these robo-citizens?

- ☐ A robo-cop
- ☐ A robo-doctor
- ☐ A robo-chef
- ☐ A robo-dogcatcher
- ☐ A robo-ballerina
- ☐ A robo-tennis pro

Rock 'n' roll back to Main Street, USA! Can you find these nifty Fifties things?

- ☐ A poodle in a skirt
- ☐ A "hula" hoop
- ☐ A sock hopping
- ☐ A real beehive hairdo
- ☐ A jukebox
- ☐ Saddle shoes
- ☐ A rock and a roll

XV